THE GAMBOLS

From The Daily Express and Sunday Express

BOOK Nº 41

by Barry Appleby

Published by Annual Concepts Limited
One High Street, Princes Risborough, Buckinghamshire HP27 OAG
under licence from Express Newspapers plc

*IF YOU'RE THINKING OF GIVING THIS
BOOK AS A PRESENT TO A FRIEND YOU
CAN CUT OFF THE PRICE HERE →*

£3·50

GEORGE TAKES A GREAT INTEREST IN GAYE'S COOKING — IT HAS SUCH A LOVELY END RESULT — USUALLY!

NEWS — GOOD AND BAD — APPOINTMENTS
GOSSIP — INFORMATION — CHATTER — TATTLE —
TIME SAVING AND TIME WASTING —
LOTS OF THINGS — WHAT SHOULD WE DO
WITHOUT THE TELEPHONE?

WHATEVER YOU SAY — MACHINES ARE GRADUALLY TAKING OVER OUR LIVES — ORDERING US ABOUT WITHOUT US NOTICING — NOT ONLY THE TELEPHONE BUT PARKING METERS AND EVEN MORE SO — THE COMPUTER

THERE ARE VERY FEW HOUSEHOLDS THESE DAYS THAT DON'T INDULGE IN DO-IT-YOURSELF — THERE'S NOTHING MORE SATISFYING THAN SEEING A NICE SMART FRESHLY DECORATED ROOM — ESPECIALLY IF YOU HAVE DONE IT TOGETHER

AND THERE'S ALWAYS THE SHOPPING

NEW CLOTHES ARE ONE OF THE MOST IMPORTANT THINGS IN GAYE'S LIFE — AND ALTHOUGH GEORGE GRUMBLES HE'S SECRETLY PROUD OF THE WAY SHE LOOKS

MONEY IS SUPPOSED TO BE
THE ROOT OF ALL EVIL—

THAT MAY BE SO—BUT
WHAT SHOULD WE
DO WITHOUT IT ?

GEORGE— GET UP—THE MORTGAGE IS DUE AND THE HIRE PURCHASE ON THE CAR..

THE POLL TAX HAS TO BE PAID AND YOU **MUST** SEND A CHEQUE FOR THE ELECTRICITY

AND THE INSURANCE ON THE CONTENTS AND WE NEED A NEW FRIDGE

WHY OH WHY IS IT THAT EVERY MONDAY MORNING I HAVE TO GIVE HIM INCENTIVES TO GO TO WORK ?

©1991 Barry Appleby   MON 5149

WONDERFUL! ALL THE BILLS ARE PAID AND WE STILL HAVE MONEY IN THE BANK

BANK BALANCE

BRRR BRRR

HULLO—OH!—WELL— I'LL GIVE HIM YOUR MESSAGE

THAT WAS THE BANK RINGING TO APOLOGISE FOR A COMPUTER ERROR

©1991 Barry Appleby   5242

THEY SAY THAT MONEY LEADS
TO MORE DOMESTIC QUARRELS
THAN ANYTHING ELSE — BUT
GEORGE AND GAYE WILL
TELL YOU THAT THEY NEVER
QUARREL — ALTHOUGH THEY
DO SOMETIMES HAVE A
LITTLE ARGUMENT

THEN THERE WAS THAT AWFUL TIME IN
OUR LIVES WHEN GAYE SUFFERED FROM
THE DELUSION THAT SHE WAS LOSING
HER SEX APPEAL

DECISIONS.... DECISIONS....
DECISIONS....

GAYE WILL TELL YOU THAT RESTORING GEORGE'S OLD CAR IS MORE THAN A HOBBY WITH HIM — IT'S BECOME AN OBSESSION

I'M NORMALLY A VERY HAPPY PERSON — WOULDN'T YOU SAY GEORGE?

OH YES

BUT I DO HAVE ONE REGRET IN MY LIFE

OH? WHAT'S THAT?

THAT I TALKED YOU OUT OF STAMP COLLECTING

©1991 Barry Appleby

28-4

GEORGE DEAR

NEVER STOP REMINDING ME.....

....HOW MUCH I ENJOY DOING THINGS TOGETHER WITH YOU

©1991 Barry Appleby 5166

GAYE HAS TRIED MANY
TIMES TO TEACH
GEORGE TO SEW —
BUT HE'S MUCH TOO
CUNNING TO LEARN

WE OFFERED TO LOOK AFTER A CAT
WHEN HER OWNER WENT ON HOLIDAY
BUT WE DIDN'T REALISE THAT THE
CAT WAS GOING TO LOOK AFTER US!

MOVING HOUSE IS THE BIGGEST UPSET
IN MOST PEOPLE'S LIVE'S — THERE'S SO
MUCH TO THINK ABOUT

GARDENING'S HARD WORK BUT IT KEEPS YOU FIT AND WELL WORTH IT

ANNIVERSARIES —
ALWAYS A CHANCE TO SHOW
YOUR LOVED ONES HOW MUCH
YOU LOVE THEM

HAVING NO CHILDREN OF OWN
WE LOVE HAVING OUR NIECE AND
NEPHEW TO VISIT US

IT SEEMS THAT OUR LIFE REVOLVES AROUND
OUR ANNUAL HOLIDAYS — NO SOONER DO
WE ARRIVE HOME THAN WE START
THINKING ABOUT NEXT YEAR'S TRIP

ONE THING THAT NEVER FAILS
TO FASCINATE GEORGE WITH
FLIVVER AND MIGGY IS THEIR
NEVER ENDING QUESTIONS

WHAT FUN IT IS TO OPEN ALL THE
PARCELS ON CHRISTMAS MORNING

GAYE IS CONVINCED THAT GEORGE IS INCAPABLE OF ENJOYING HIMSELF WITHOUT GETTING DIRTY

NEVERTHELESS
THEY'RE REALLY
VERY FOND
OF
EACH OTHER

.... AND SO WE COME TO THE END OF
THE GAMBOLS BOOK NUMBER 41 —
IT'S BEEN NICE HAVING YOU WITH US
— WE HOPE YOU'VE ENJOYED IT
AS MUCH AS WE HAVE

©1992 Barry Appleby

ISBN 1 874507 04X
Printed in Italy